P9-DCS-856

This Book Belongs To:

____

In Him

Confessions

For Kids

Stanley Moore III

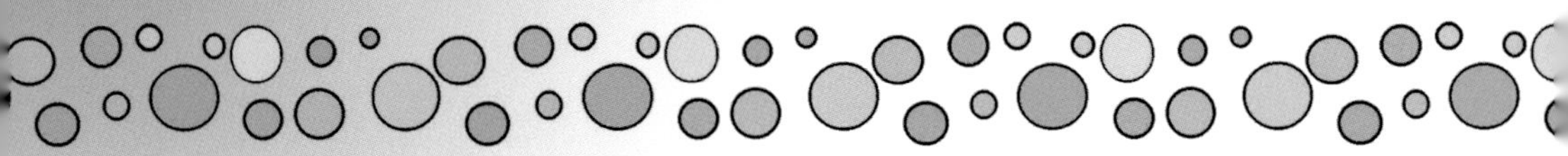

In Him Confessions
Daily Poem Confessions for Kids
ISBN 0-9706014-2-5

Printed in Korea by www.asianprinting.com

All scripture is taken from the King James Version of the Bible.

Stanley Moore Publications
18414 NW 9th Street
Pembroke Pines, Fl 33029

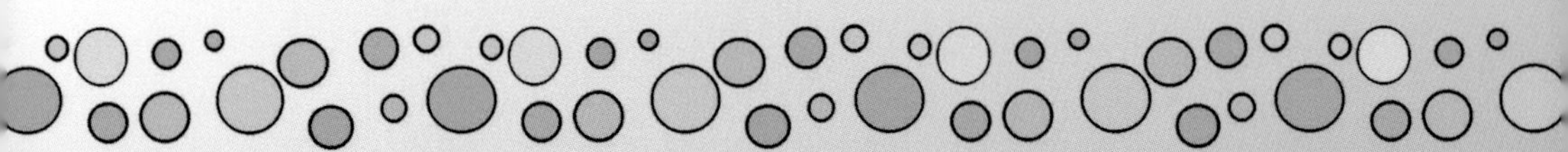

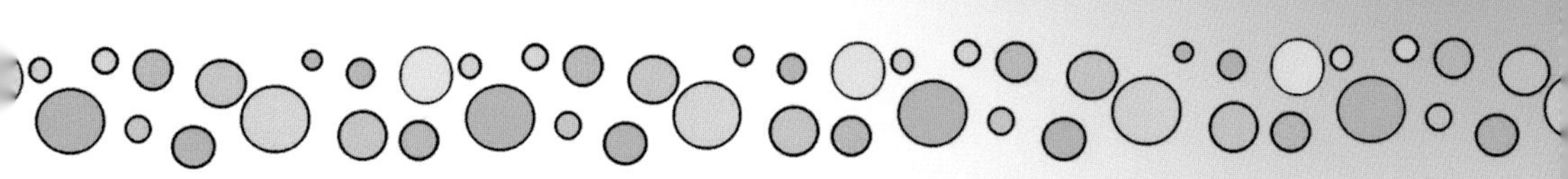

About the Book

In Him Confessions help young people understand God's Word and the provisions He has made for them when they are in Christ. With one poem for each day of the month, these poems give children the opportunity to speak the Word over their lives on a daily basis, as well as learn what they have been given and who they are in Him. The devil does not wait until children are grown to attack them, so we must not wait until they are grown to get the Word into them.

These poems are not only powerful teaching tools. They train young people how to take hold of what is theirs in the Word through their own words. The Bible says, "Death and life are in the power of the tongue," so it is crucial that you have your children speak over their lives what God says about them.

I can!

Philippians 4:13

I can do all things through Christ which strengtheneth me.

Through Christ, my Lord, I can do anything.
I'll just trust in God, like David with his sling.
I can do good in school, climb any tree,
For I know Jesus Christ is strengthening me.
I cannot be conquered; I can't be defeated.
When I start a project, God helps me complete it.
I won't give up, or say "I don't know how."
With Christ as my strength, "I can'ts" aren't allowed.

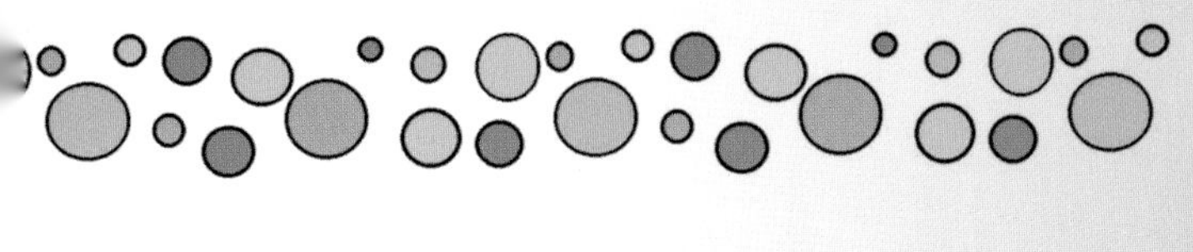

Wisdom in Him

Colossians 2:3

In whom are hid all the treasures of wisdom and knowledge.

In Christ I get my wisdom and knowledge. In Him I know I'm smart.
When I don't know, I'll forget my head, and just look to my heart.
Just like Jesus, I increase in wisdom each day with God and man.
Though a problem or test may look tough, with God I know I can.
I have the mind of Christ and God's Spirit in me each day.
If God can part the whole Red Sea, He can help me get an A.
I may not know it all in school, but with God's help I know I'll learn it.
God's help and knowledge is a gift; I accept it, but I can't earn it.

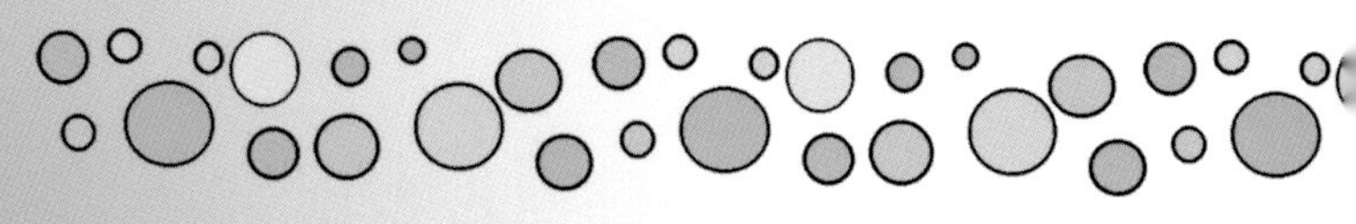

Enriched in Everything

I Corinthians 1:5

That in every thing ye are enriched by him, in all utterance, and in all knowledge;

In every area of my life, in everything I do,
I'm enriched by Jesus Christ, the One who helps me make it through.
I enrich or I increase in stature, knowledge and love each day.
My favor's growing constantly, and I can have what I say.
He enriches my spirit daily with revelation knowledge from His Word.
My mind is enriched and renewed day by day; I remember all I have heard.
Enrich means to make me richer; God supplies all of my needs.
He'll enrich my harvest, but first I have to sow my seed.
He can enrich me in my health; Moses' eyes weren't even dimmed.
In everything, no matter what, I am always enriched in Him.

The Righteousness of God

2 Corinthians 5:21

For he hath made him to be sin for us, who knew no sin; that we might be made the righteousness of God in him.

All my sins were washed away when Christ died on the cross.
So I can live a joyful life, He suffered so much loss.
Christ took our sins and sickness and our pain at Calvary.
Now I can live without it because I've been set free.
I'm the righteousness of God; I'm out of Satan's clutch.
According to James 5:16, my prayers avail much.
God doesn't see my sins. To Him they've passed away.
I'm righteous and delivered, and God's with me all the way.

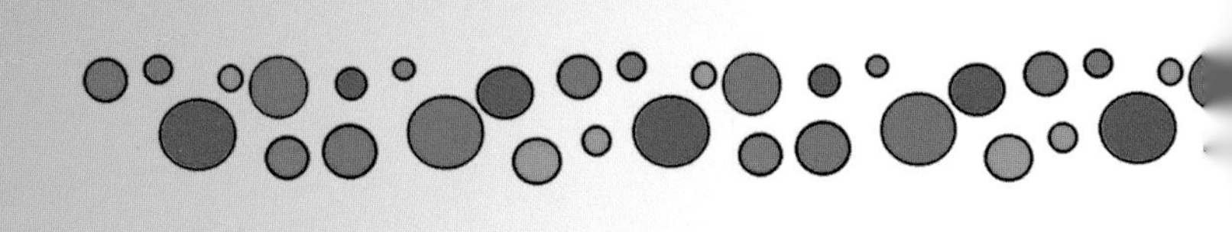

Redeemed

Galatians 3:13

Christ hath redeemed us from the curse of the law, being made a curse for us: for it is written, Cursed is every one that hangeth on a tree:

Christ set me free from the curse of the law, being made a curse for me.
For it was written, "Cursed is everyone that hangeth on a tree."
The curse of the law is talked about in Deuteronomy.
It says the curse is spiritual death, sickness, and even poverty.
So since I'm redeemed from it, there's no way I can be poor.
Sickness can't live in my body or come near me anymore.
And since Christ is inside me, second death has got to go.
That means I'll go to heaven, and I want everyone to know:
Satan's rule on us is over, and in Jesus name he has to flee.
I won't accept his curse, since Jesus took it all for me.

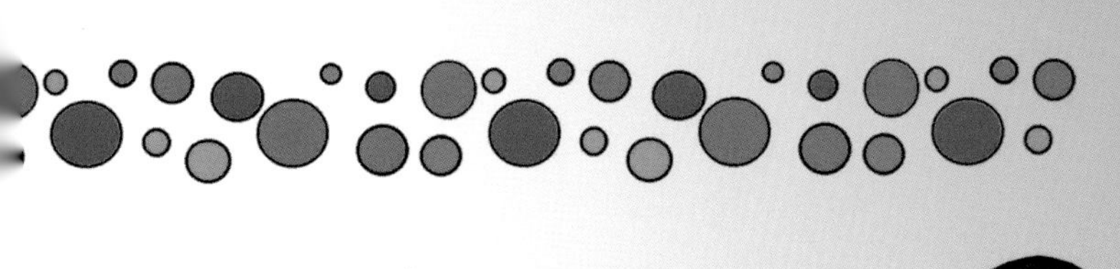

Perfect Love

I John 2:5

But whoso keepeth his word, in him verily is the love of God perfected: hereby know we that we are in him.

When people look at me, they see God's love shining through,
I keep my word and the Word of God because I know it's true.
I know that I am in Him by Christ's love that is inside me,
I love my neighbor as myself and prefer the one beside me.
Because I keep His Word, in me the love of God's perfected.
With God's love and favor I know I can't be beaten or rejected.
People know that I'm a Christian by the love of God I show.
As I walk in the love and share it, it will begin to grow.

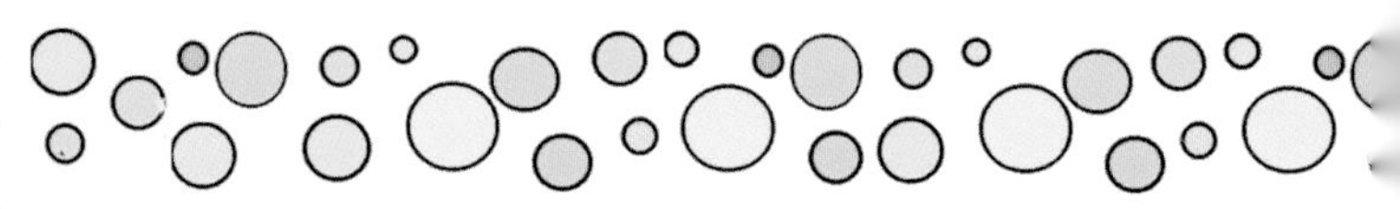

Peace that Passes Understanding

Philipians 4:6, 7

Be careful for nothing; but in every thing by prayer and supplication with thanksgiving let your requests be made known unto God. And the peace of God, which passeth all understanding, shall keep your hearts and minds through Christ Jesus.

I'm not careful for anything; I cast my worries on the Lord.
I know there's nothing He can't do or a thing He can't afford.
I just pray and thank God for what I need, and then I rest assured.
That He'll watch over and take care of me like He said in His Word.
Worry defeats faith in God, and is a tool that's used by Satan.
I won't worry, but I make requests known to God through my supplication.
When it looks like time to worry or when things start to fall apart,
I don't fret but let the peace of God rule in my mind and heart.

Do All in the Name of the Lord

Colossians 3:17

And whatsoever ye do in word or deed, do all in the name of the Lord Jesus, giving thanks to God and the Father by him.

I do all in the Name of the Lord; I'm representing Christ.
I speak the Word and show God's love by always acting nice.
I thank the Lord for all my talents and all He's placed in me.
Whatever I do in His Name, I have the victory.
I love my God and His Son who was sent for me and you.
Everything shall be successful, that I set out to do.
I don't do those things that are of the world, which the devil wants me to.
I give thanks to God and promote His Name in all I say and do.

Strong In the Lord

Ephesians 6:10

Finally, my brethren, be strong in the Lord, and in the power of his might.

I'm not strong alone; I can't fight my own fight.
But I'm strong in the Lord and in the power of His might.
It's in God I get strength. He's helping me each day.
He helps me to go on, be strong, and He shows me the way.
The joy of the Lord is my might in Him, and it is my strength.
For giving me joy and keeping me safe I always give Him thanks.
I don't trust in my muscles, but in the Word as my sword.
It is not by my own might, but I am strong in the Lord.

Whatever I Need

Philippians 4:19

But my God shall supply all your need according to his riches in glory by Christ Jesus.

My God shall give me whatever I need.
If I ask it of Him it shall be guaranteed.
I know He is rich; what I need He'll provide.
Whatever I want is already supplied.
I just have to ask, and He gives it to me,
There are no strings attached; it's given for free.
It can't be too big, too great, or too grand.
God supplies all my needs, just like He planned.

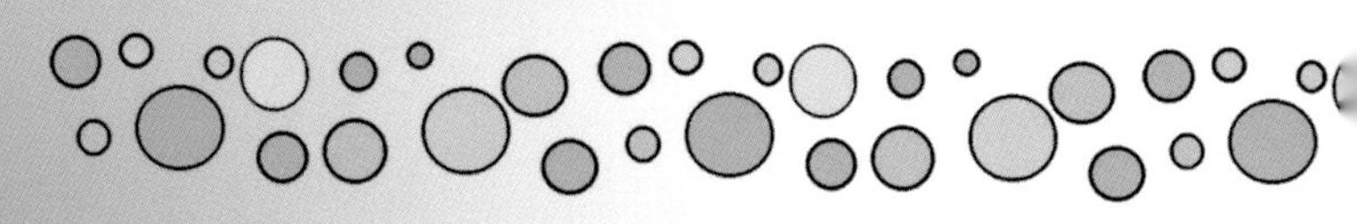

God So Loved Me

John 3:15-16

That whosoever believeth in him should not perish, but have eternal life. For God so loved the world, that he gave his only begotten Son, that whosoever believeth in him should not perish, but have everlasting life.

I know that God must love me; He sent His only son.
He would have sent Jesus down here, if I were the only one.
I believe in His Son Jesus; that He died on the cross.
Now I'm God's. I belong to him, and Satan's not my boss.
I'm so glad He sent his Son; I have everlasting life.
I'll go up to heaven where I'm free from sin and strife.
When I became born again I unlocked all God's provisions.
Now I'll just possess them and make the right decisions.
I know that I won't go to hell and that Satan's a deceiver.
I'll tell others about God's only Son, and save the unbelievers.

Victorious Through Him

I Corinthians 15:57

But thanks be to God, which giveth us the victory through our Lord Jesus Christ.

I thank God each and every day, for all He's said and done.
He's given me the victory and makes me number one.
The devil tries to keep us down and make us feel defeated.
But I know I'm victorious; my course will be completed.
I'm thankful that I know with God I have already won,
I have become victorious through His
precious Son.
There's no way that I can lose,
with Jesus as my guide.
I'll always have the victory
with Jesus on my side.

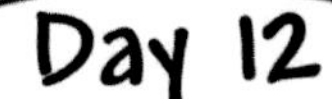

Made Unto Us

I Corinthians 1:30

But of him are ye in Christ Jesus, who of God is made unto us wisdom, and righteousness, and sanctification, and redemption:

I know that I am in Christ my Lord, in Whom I've been so blessed.
Made unto me are wisdom, redemption, and even righteousness.
I have sanctification and redemption; I've been washed by the blood.
Jesus knows that He can use me, and He wants to be my bud.
I believe by God He was made to be wisdom unto me.
I'll be wise and I do great in school, whatever it may be.
He was made unto me righteousness, the Bible also has to say.

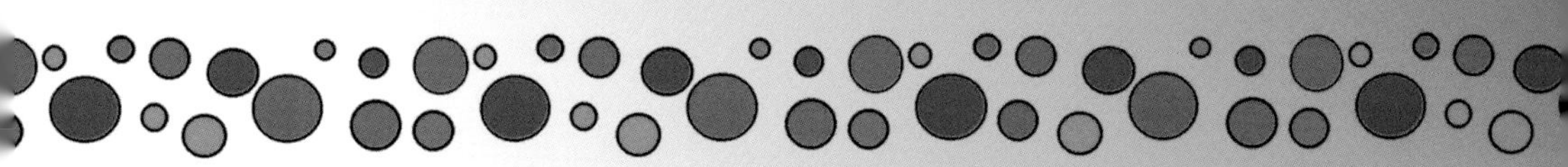

This is right standing with the Father and I'm effective when I pray.
I'm so glad that Jesus was sent for me. Oh yes I am so blessed.
Made unto me are wisdom, sanctification, and righteousness.

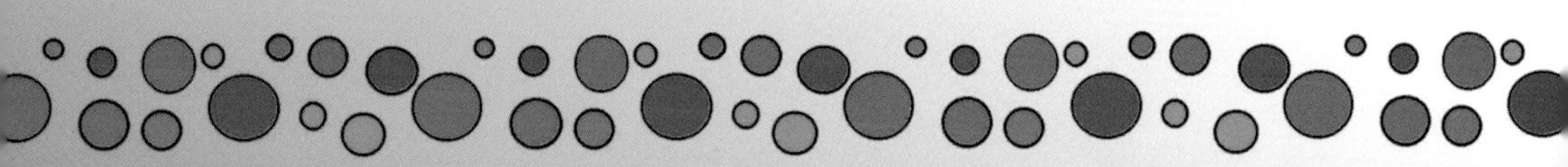

Blessed With All Spiritual Blessings

Ephesians 1:3

Blessed be the God and Father of our Lord Jesus Christ, who hath blessed us with all spiritual blessings in heavenly places in Christ:

I bless the Lord who blesses me because I do believe.
Everything of God's a gift that I must just receive.
Not only am I blessed on earth; I have spiritual blessings up above.
I've had it all from my new birth because of God's great love.
I look into God's Word to find His promises for me.
Then I agree, and I accept it, and it becomes reality.
God not only gives me things on earth but the things that matter most,
Like the riches up in heaven, and His love and Holy Ghost.
Once I accept His gifts, my God will do the rest.
I thank God and rejoice because I know I'm blessed.

Peace In Him

John 16:33

These things I have spoken unto you, that in me ye might have peace. In the world ye shall have tribulation: but be of good cheer; I have overcome the world.

I know that I have peace, through the Lord, Christ my Savior.
I'll stay calm and still, and I won't have a "worry-hurry" behavior.
Though the world is full of troubles, though it's full of fear,
I'm standing on the Word of God; I'll be of good cheer.
I don't have to fret, and right now, I cast on Him my cares,
He keeps me calm and He gives me peace in the midst of despair.
Although there's trouble in the world, they have been overthrown.
I'll be peaceful and stay calm; in him I'm not alone.

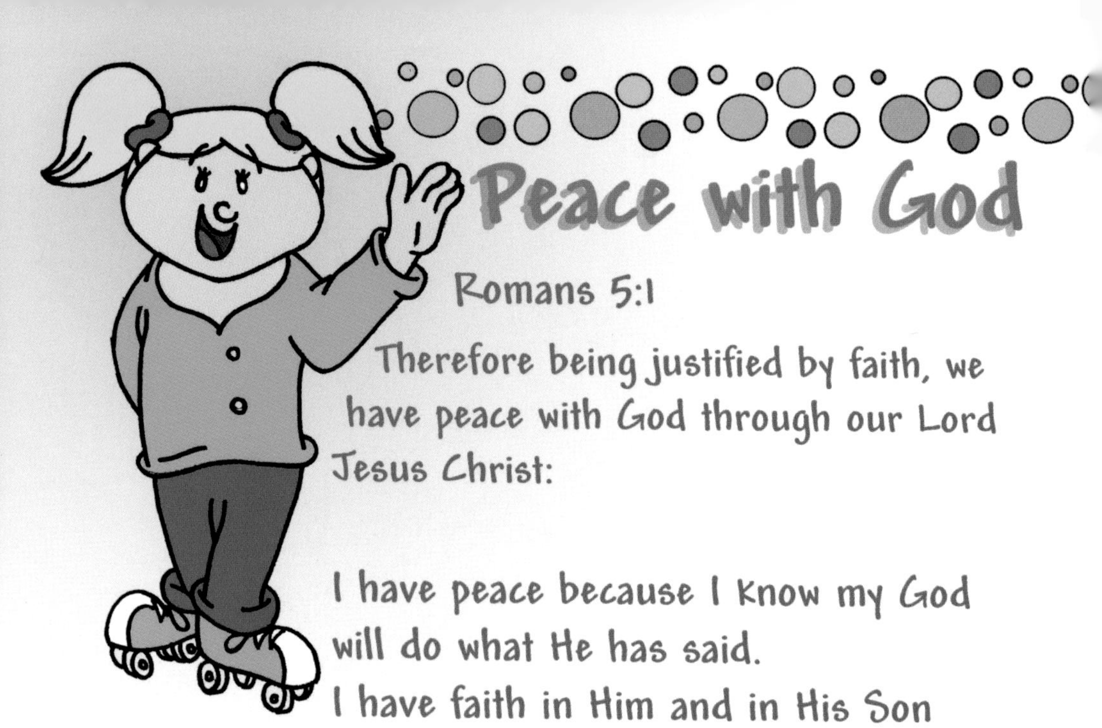

Peace with God

Romans 5:1

Therefore being justified by faith, we have peace with God through our Lord Jesus Christ:

I have peace because I know my God
will do what He has said.
I have faith in Him and in His Son
Who's risen from the dead.
I don't worry what happens in the world. I know that
I'm protected.
By faith in Him I'm justified, or righteous and accepted.
I'm not concerned about things I don't have, or
something that I need.
God will supply because I tithe and will harvest my
sown seed.
It's through Christ that I have peace; I can't get it any
other way.
Though the world is full of troubles, I listen to what
God has to say.
I don't depend on the alarm, my own mind, or the police.
God is taking care of me, so with Him I can have peace.

No Condemnation

Romans 8:1

There is therefore now no condemnation to them which are in Christ Jesus, who walk not after the flesh, but after the Spirit.

I don't associate with Satan; I walk after the Spirit.
I repent if I do something wrong, and I know God will hear it.
Whatever I repent of, He'll wash away since He's forgiving.
I want the death of my Lord Jesus Christ to be worth my living.
Since I am in Him, no condemnation's in my life.
That's when I feel bad if I did wrong or fought in strife.
Satan tries to use these sins to make me feel bad, depressed or blue.
But if I ask, God forgives and forgets, and that means I should too.
Once I repent, I know God forgives, and I give that sin no contemplation.
Since I'm in Christ and I walk after Him, there is now no more condemnation.

He Hears Me

I John 5:14

And this is the confidence that we have in him, that, if we ask any thing according to his will, he heareth us:

I have confidence in Christ; I know that He comes through.
I obey the Word, believe it, and I know that it is true.
I know the will of God and that His will is in His Word.
When I pray according to it, I know that I'll be heard.
I can ask Him anything and I know He is my source.
I love the Word and love the Lord, Who keeps me straight on course.
God cares for me and loves me. He listens when I pray.
And since He listens all the time, I'm watching what I say.
Through my spirit and the Word I know His will and I pray by it.
Whatever I ask, big or small, I know that He'll supply it.

By His Stripes

I Peter 2:24

Who his own self bare our sins in his own body on the tree, that we, being dead to sins, should live unto righteousness: by whose stripes ye were healed.

Jesus bore my sickness and my sin back at Calvary.
My unrighteousness was washed away when He hung on the tree.
By His stripes I was healed. I was healed that day.
I accept my healing now, for He's already had to pay.
I won't put up with sickness, sniffles, coughs or colds.
I just say it's gone and tell the devil, "That sickness stuff is old."
Righteousness is right standing with God; in Him do I abide.
So I'm righteous and I'm healed; this is why Jesus died.

I'm Anointed

I John 2:27

But the anointing which ye have received of him abideth in you...

The anointing I've received from Christ now abides in me.
I can heal the sick, and with God I'll set the captives free.
I received this great anointing like I received Christ in my heart.
I can do the works that He did and play my important part.
The anointing breaks the yokes, and since the anointing is in me,
I can break the bondage in the world, whatever it might be.
I'm anointed and no matter what the devil tries to do.
The Bible says, "The anointing ...received of Him abides in you."

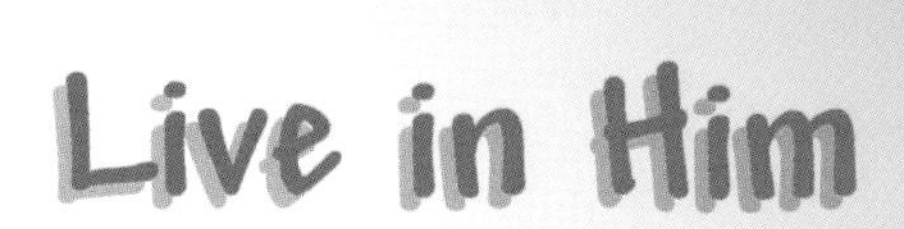

Live in Him

Acts 17:28

For in him we live, and move, and have our being....

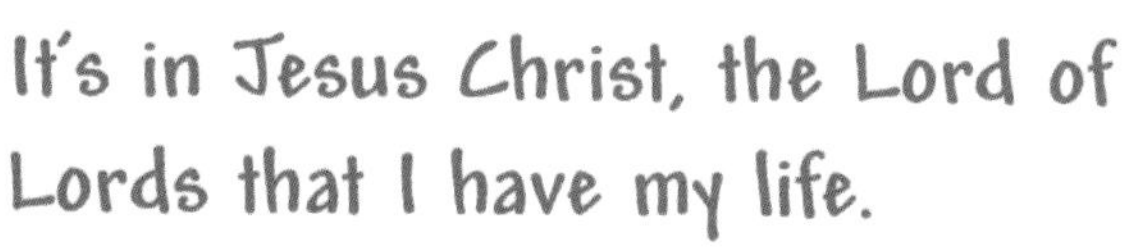

It's in Jesus Christ, the Lord of Lords that I have my life.
He keeps me calm, in perfect love, and out of any strife.
God gives me energy, gives me might, and air for my next breath.
I have health and life and strength each day because of His own death.
I'm powered by the Almighty, in Him I live and move.
In Him I'm renewed day by day. I continue to improve.
I have strength for the impossible tasks that I'll face this hour,
In Him I have my being. What a vast storehouse of power!

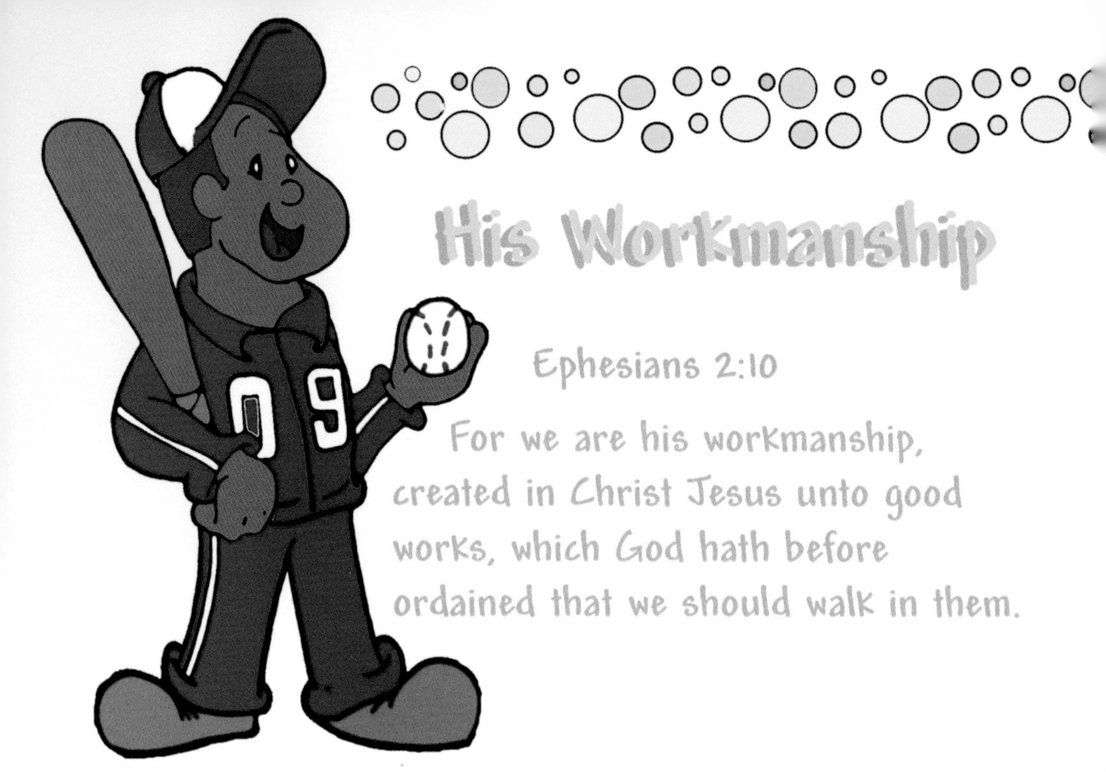

His Workmanship

Ephesians 2:10

For we are his workmanship, created in Christ Jesus unto good works, which God hath before ordained that we should walk in them.

I'm the workmanship of God. I'm his very own creation.
He's made me for this specific time, this very situation.
When God made the world, He said that all of it was good.
So I don't have to feel down, depressed, or misunderstood.
God has a course for me to run, good works before ordained.
With Christ I'll finish all the works and walk in faith unfeigned.
I'll be what God wants me to be: a pilot, policeman, or teacher.
I'm the workmanship of my Father. I'm a beautiful new creature.

Delivered From Darkness

Colossians 1:13, 14

Who hath delivered us from the power of darkness, and hath translated us into the kingdom of his dear Son: In whom we have redemption through his blood, even the forgiveness of sins:

God delivered me from darkness; Jesus rose again and won.
I am translated into the kingdom of God's dear and only Son.
I'm delivered from worry, sickness, sin, and all of my cares.
I laugh right in the devil's face and won't take his despair.
Through His precious blood, shed for me, I have been redeemed.
My sins have been forgiven, no matter how bad they may seem.
I'm delivered from the power of darkness; I'm forgiven from my sins.
I'm translated into His kingdom where the devil can't enter in.

The Greater One's In Me

I John 4:4

Ye are of God, little children, and have overcome them: because greater is he that is in you, than he that is in the world.

I'm a child of God, and like a father helps his son.
God is watching over me, and He is the greater One.
He is greater than the sin, disease and all the devil has planned.
He's inside of me protecting me with His great and mighty hand.
Although the devil has some power, he is no match for the Lord.
The devil doesn't have a chance; the Word of God's my sword.
I'm an over-comer and I can make the devil flee.
I'm not afraid of he who's in the world; the Greater One's in me.

The True Vine

John 15:5, 7

I am the vine, ye are the branches...If ye abide in me, and my words abide in you, ye shall ask what ye will, and it shall be done unto you.

I live and I abide in Him.
I am the branch; He is the vine.
His life, His love's inside of me,
What I ask shall soon be mine.
I abide in God, and His Word's inside of me.
Whatever it is that I ask soon shall come to be.
Whether it's a bike or an A on the math test,
I ask, and then believe; and my God will do the rest.
I ask, and I step out in faith; I know it will be fine.
For His Word's in me, I am the branch, and He is the vine.

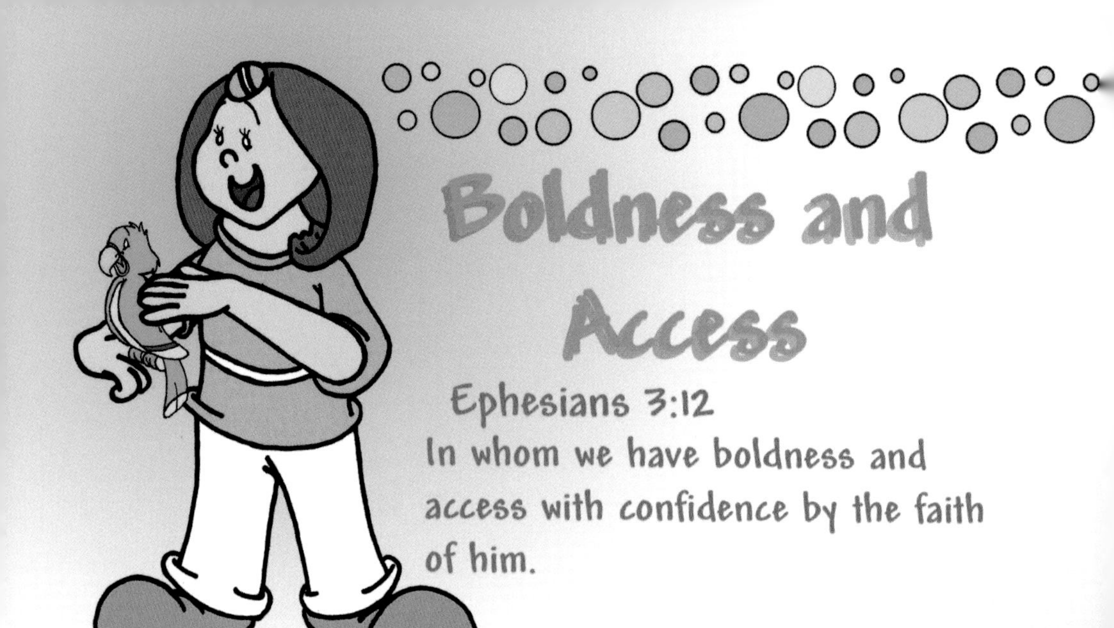

Boldness and Access

Ephesians 3:12

In whom we have boldness and access with confidence by the faith of him.

I have boldness in my life; I'm not afraid to do God's will.
I can tell my friends of Jesus, how He rose once He was killed.
I have access to the power of my Lord and His great throne.
When the devil comes against me, I know I'm not alone.
I have confidence in Christ. I know He'll do what He said.
I won't give in to the world, and each day I'm being led.
I'll be a witness in my school; I have favor and I'm blessed.
I am confident in the faith of Him; I have boldness and access.

More Than a Conqueror

Romans 8:37

Nay, in all these things we are more than conquerors through him that loved us.

I am more than a conqueror through Jesus my Lord.
The devil's defeated; God's Word is my sword.
But I'm more than a conqueror - much more, you see.
It's not that I'm strong, but Christ inside of me.
We conquer, overcome by the blood of the Lamb.
Because of Him that loved us, the devil must scram.
The battle's the Lord's; the victory is ours.
We've conquered Satan and all evil powers,
We're more than conquerors. We have room to spare.
Through Him that loved us, we don't have to be scared.

Walk in Him

Colossians 2:6, 10

As ye have therefore received Christ Jesus the Lord, so walk ye in him... And ye are complete in him, which is the head of all principality and power:

I walk in the Lord, in His power, in His might.
I'm an example to my friends; in my school I am a light.
Jesus Christ is part of me, with Him my life is complete.
I walk and talk the Word of God to everyone I meet.
I don't have to be afraid; God is with me every hour.
I'm walking with the Head of principalities and power.
This power's greater than the devil and his sickness or his sin.
Because I have received Christ as Lord, each day I walk in him.

Always Triumphant

2 Corinthians 2:14

Now thanks be unto God, which always causeth us to triumph in Christ, and maketh manifest the savour of his knowledge by us in every place.

It's such a reassuring thought that the devil can't defeat me.
No matter what he tries, there's no way he'll beat me.
When the devil starts to tell me that there just isn't any way,
I tell him what the Bible says and point out the Word always!
The Scripture says "in Christ." I can't triumph on my own.
He is causing me to triumph. I'm not doing it alone.
He makes manifest His knowledge every place and every day.
I'm so thankful to the Father, and I will triumph always.

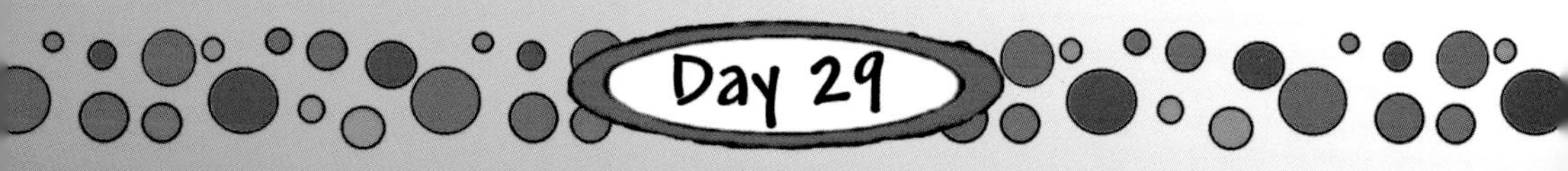

The Law of Life

Romans 8:2

For the law of the Spirit of life in Christ Jesus hath made me free from the law of sin and death.

I value God's Word highly, and I love to sit and hear it.
In Christ there is a freeing law of life of the Spirit.
I'm in Christ and I am under this law, so I'm free from death and sin.
Since I confess and walk in the light of the law, no diseases enter in.
Every bad germ that hits my body must die in Jesus' name.
I've been set free from disease, and it must die the same.
This law means Christ protects me, and though I may die some day.
The law of death means hell and spiritual death, which left after I prayed--
Prayed to accept Christ that is, the One who gives me my next breath.
He's helping me, and set me free from the law of sin and death.

A New Creature

2 Corinthians 5:17

Therefore if any man be in Christ, he is a new creature: old things are passed away; behold, all things are become new.

I'm a new creature, a new species; a brand-spanking-new creation.
I'm not made-over or reformed; God made me new with my salvation.
I have the life, the nature, and strength of God on the inside of me.
Sin and sickness are wiped out; I'm filled with God's ability.
Although my body on the outside didn't seem to change, God's inside me, and my spirit has been completely rearranged.
All the bad stuff that I've done is fully washed away.
I'm a new creature, God's creation, and I'll never go astray.

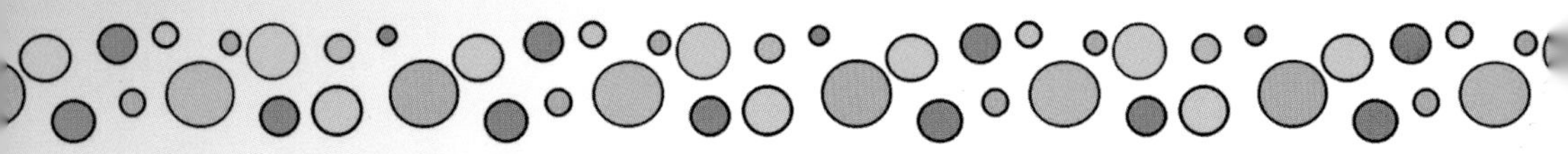

About the Author

Stanley Moore, age fourteen, was born and raised in South Florida. Not only is he author of the book, he also illustrated and designed the characters and pages. In Him Confessions for Kids is his first book but he is excited to continue writing and do all that God wants him to. He is the son of Stan and Teresa Moore, and has two sisters, Victoria and Olivia. Stanley is a member of Words of Life Fellowship Church in North Miami Beach, Florida, where his grandfather and father pastor. Stanley has a desire to reach the young, the lost, and the world using the talents and dreams God has given him.

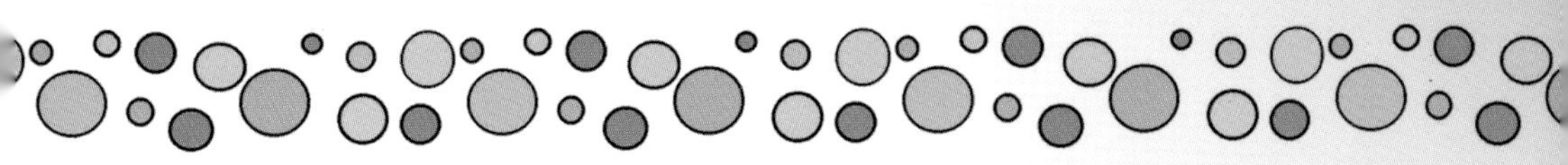

Born into God's Family

There is only one way to unlock the provisions God has made for you "in Him", and that's to be born again. Being born again does not mean your body will change, but your spirit man, the real you on the inside, becomes a new person. It doesn't matter how many good or bad things you have done, Jesus said you must be born again.

By confessing Jesus as Lord, and believing in your heart that he died and rose again for you, you can become a child of God. When you ask Jesus Christ to come into your heart, you accept the free gift of eternal life, and enter into the family of God. Just pray this simple prayer out loud to make Jesus your Lord.
You'll never regret it. Just say,

Dear Heavenly Father.
You said that whoever shall call upon the name of the Lord, shall be saved.
Right now I'm calling on you, believing on you, and asking you to forgive me for any wrong thing I've ever done.
I confess with my mouth that Jesus Christ is Lord.
I believe in my heart, that he rose from the dead.
Jesus, you are my Lord.
From this day forward,
I'm living for you.
And you're living in me.
Thank you for saving me, in Jesus mighty name, Amen.

If you prayed this prayer I'd like to personally welcome you to the Kingdom of God. Let someone know about it, call us if you'd like, and start your brand new life for the Lord. Everything in this book is now rightfully yours and don't let the devil tell you otherwise. Read your Bible, find a good Bible church, and start praying to and trusting in the Lord.

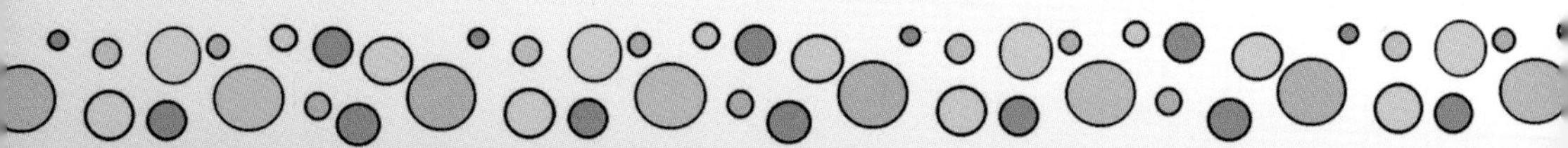

To order additional books, find out
about new material, or contact the
author, please call: 305 653 8155 ext. 103,
email at: stanleymoorepublications@msn.com
or write to:

Stanley Moore Publications
18414 NW 9th Street
Pembroke Pines, Fl 33029